TOM and JERRY
ANNUAL 1973

70P

CONTENTS

Published in Great Britain by World Distributors (Manchester) Limited
P.O. Box 111, 12 Lever Street, Manchester M60 1TS.
by arrangement with Western Publishing Company Inc., Racine,
Wisconsin, U.S.A.

PRINTED IN THE NETHERLANDS

SBN 7235 0160 2

11

13

SO, TUFFY AND JERRY ARE THE FIRST HAPPY RESIDENTS OF SWANKY ACRES...

THIS IS THE LIFE!

BAH! I GAVE THAT HOUSE AWAY FOR PUBLICITY! BUT GIVING IT TO MICE IS JUST *BAD* PUBLICITY! I'LL BE A LAUGHINGSTOCK!

(SIGH!) BUT IF I THROW THEM OUT IT'LL BE EVEN *WORSE* PUBLICITY! I WISH I KNEW SOMEBODY WHO COULD GET RID OF MICE!

SO THIS' IS WHERE THE MICE WON THAT HOME! PRETTY SWANKY! I GUESS THEY'LL NEVER COME BACK TO MY PLACE NOW!

I ACTUALLY MISS THEM! NOBODY TO TEASE AND CHASE!

HEY! YOU'RE A CAT, AREN'T YOU?

THE LAST TIME I LOOKED I WAS!

HOW'D YOU LIKE TO GET RID OF A COUPLE OF MICE FOR ME BY THROWING THEM OUT OF A HOUSE?

IF YOU MEAN THOSE MICE IN THERE, I'D LOVE TO! THEN THEY'D HAVE TO COME BACK TO MY PLACE!

SWELL!

DO IT HOWEVER YOU WANT TO, BUT LEAVE MY NAME OUT OF IT! I'LL GIVE YOU A REWARD IF YOU SUCCEED!

Tom and Jerry ALMOST A GENIUS

HEY! THAT FAST-DRYING CEMENT MADE THEM LOOK JUST LIKE LITTLE STATUES!

STATUES! WHY NOT? HEH, HEH! IT LOOKS LIKE OLD TOM IS ENTERING THAT SCULPTURING CONTEST AFTER ALL!

HEY, BOSS! THAT'S THE CAT WHO TOOK THE CORNERSTONE FOR OUR BUILDING! I SAW HIM!

WHY DIDN'T YOU STOP HIM?

IT WAS MY LUNCH HOUR! AND I CAN'T HELP YOU CHASE HIM NOW CAUSE I'M ON MY COFFEE BREAK!

GRRR!

SHORTLY...

NOTHING OUTSTANDING YET!

HERE'S THE JUDGE! I GOT HERE JUST IN TIME!

THESE ARE INCREDIBLE! THEY LOOK JUST LIKE REAL MICE!

HELP! WE ARE REAL MICE!

AMAZING! THEY LOOK LIKE THEY COULD TALK!

Tom and Jerry: THE UNWANTED FORTUNE

Tom and Jerry — BLUEBEARD'S CLOSE SHAVE

THAT SHOULD DO IT!

NOW TO UNROLL MY OCEAN SCENE WALLPAPER!

FLOOP!

SNICKER!

QUICK, JERRY! LET'S LOOK OUT AND SEE WHERE WE ARE!

OKAY, TUFFY!

GULP!

AND YOU SAID THERE WERE NO PIRATES!

WELL, PIRATES OR NO PIRATES, WE CAN'T JUST SIT AROUND AND DO NOTHING! LET ME THINK!

WELL, MATES, DO YOU BELIEVE IN PIRATES, NOW?

Y-YES, SIR!

SLAM!

PLIK!

HAAAAAA!

HEY, JERRY, WHAT'S THAT ON YOUR HEAD?

ᴵLater...

IMAGINE SOMEBODY PAYING FOR HAVING A BOAT TOWED TO THE OCEAN ...AND THEN RIGHT BACK TO THEIR OWN BACK YARD!

THANKS, FELLAS! JUST SEND THE BILL TO TOM!

HE'S COMING TO, JERRY!

I'LL TAKE OVER NOW!

WAIT, FELLAS, YOU CAN'T *DO* THIS TO ME, CAN YOU?

SURE, TOM, IT'S EASY!

AND NOW IT'S TIME TO WALK THE PLANK!

BUT I CAN'T SWIM! IN FACT, I'M TOO WEAK TO WALK!

COME ON, TOM! THIS SHOULD BE A CINCH FOR AN OLD PIRATE LIKE YOU!

BUT—BUT, I DROWN EASY!

SPLASH! SPLASH!

AH, JUST LISTEN TO THOSE WAVES BECKONING YOU ON!

GULP!

TOM and JERRY

TO BUILD A BETTER MOUSETRAP

REMEMBER, FRIENDS, OUR FAMOUS QUOTATION FOR TODAY— "BUILD A BETTER MOUSETRAP AND THE WORLD WILL BEAT A PATH TO YOUR DOOR!"

SOUNDS LOGICAL!

IN FACT, THAT'S JUST WHAT THIS WORLD NEEDS... A *BETTER MOUSETRAP!* AND I'M JUST THE CAT *WHO CAN BUILD IT!*

WHAT'RE YOU DRAWING, TOM?

A KITE, MAYBE?

QUIET!

AW, COME ON, TOM... PLEASE TELL US!

YEAH! YOU'VE GOT OUR CURIOSITY ALL AROUSED!

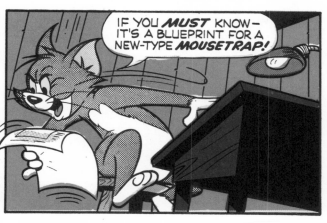

IF YOU *MUST* KNOW— IT'S A BLUEPRINT FOR A NEW-TYPE *MOUSETRAP!*

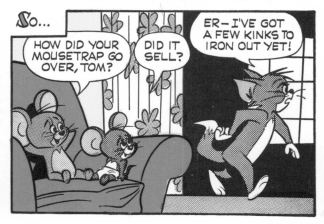

44

45

46

TOM and JERRY *BUSY BUDDIES*

SPECIAL SALE OF IMPORTED FLYING FISH TODAY ONLY

JUST A FEW OF THESE SENSATIONAL TROPICAL SPECIMENS LEFT! HURRY! HURRY!

PETE'S PET EMPORIUM

TUFFY, LET'S BUY ONE! IT WOULD BE A BALL TO WATCH IT SAILING IN AND OUT OF A POND!

BUT WE DON'T HAVE A POND, JERRY, AND BY THE TIME TWO LITTLE WEAK MICE LIKE US COULD DIG ONE, THE FISH WOULD ALL BE SOLD!

LET'S ASK TOM TO DO THE DIGGING FOR US!

HUH? I WAS PLANNING ON *THEM* DOING SOME THINGS FOR *ME* TODAY!

I'LL GO INTO MY STRICKEN KITTEN ACT!

AAACK! STRANGLE! GASP!

I'M GOING TO F-FAINT!

A FINE TIME FOR THAT GOON TO SWOON!

I'LL HAVE TO REVIVE HIM IF HE'S GOING TO DO ANY DIGGING!

THIS CHAIR COULDN'T HAVE BEEN IN A BETTER PLACE FOR A PLOP!

PLOP!

55

MOUSE MUSKETEERS
JOUST FOR FUN

58

TO A JOU ... *OUCH!*

HE DID NOT FINISH THE CHALLENGE SO...

WE DO NOT HAVE TO FIGHT HIM YET!

I DON'T KNOW WHAT THAT MUTT DID, BUT I'LL SEE HE DOESN'T DO IT AGAIN!

FETCH THE STICK, BOY!

PERCHANCE WE CAN GET A HORSE BEFORE M'SIEUR POOSYCAT CAN CHALLENGE US AGAIN!

I DO NOT NEED A STICK, BUT I MUST DO MY DOG-DUTY AND RETRIEVE IT!

HYUK! HYUK! I WILL SHUT HIM IN THE CASTLE!

NOW I CAN CHALLENGE THE LITTLE CHUMPS WITHOUT INTERFERENCE!

SLAM!

IF PEOPLE DON'T WANT HOLES BURNED IN THEIR DOORS, THEY SHOULDN'T SHUT ME IN!

WHO PUT THIS RIVER HERE?

SPLOOSH!

ROYAL STABLES

MAYHAPS WE WILL FIND A FIERCE CHARGER IN HERE THAT WE MIGHT *BORROW*, MY FRIEND!

MY "*FUR*" GOT WASHED OFF, BUT I WILL BE A GOOD DOG AND TAKE THE STICK TO THE POOSYCAT!

I MUST HURRY BEFORE THOSE MUSKETEERS GET A HORSE THEY CAN BEAT ME WITH!

HOLD, *VARLETS!*

SO HE IS PESTERING MY FRIENDS AGAIN!

I CHALLENGE YOU TO A... ACK!(COUGH!)

I WILL MAKE HIM CHOKE ON SOME DRAGON SMOKE!

POOF!

EGAD! HE LOST HIS DISGUISE!

HEY! WHAT GOES ON HERE?

QUICK, LITTLE ONE! BEFORE THE SMOKE SCREEN LIFTS! NO ONE MUST KNOW WHAT HE IS!

IT'S CLEARING UP NOW!

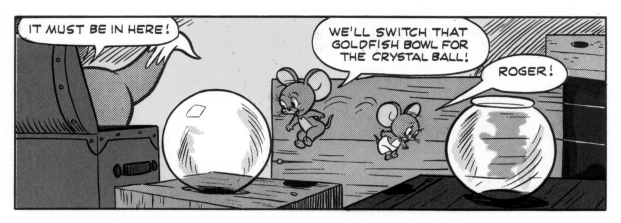

I'LL BE THE FRAIDYCAT AND WAIT HERE WHILE YOU TWO GO AND BRING BACK A GOLDEN ANIMAL IMAGE!

WE'LL HAVE TO MAKE HIM THINK WE'RE TRYING!

HI, LITTLE FRIENDS! DID YOU COME TO LIVE IN THE OLD INDIAN CAVES?

NO! BUT MAYBE YOU CAN HELP US WITH OUR PROBLEM!

THERE'S A CAT THAT SENT US AFTER A GOLDEN ANIMAL IMAGE!

HMM...THERE ARE NO GOLDEN ANIMALS HERE, BUT...

...THERE ARE PLENTY OF JUST PLAIN LIVE-TYPE ONES!

THEY'RE NICE, BUT THEY WON'T HELP US!

SURE, WE WILL! WHAT CAN WE DO FOR YOU, STRANGERS?

HMM....I HAVE A FOXY-TYPE PLAN! WE'LL FOOL THAT FOOLISH FELINE...

...BY THE USE OF THIS FOOL'S GOLD!

BUT THE CAT'LL FIND OUT IT'S NOT A REAL GOLD BUNNY!

FOOL'S GOLD

LITTLE QUACKER
THE CASE OF THE MISLAID EGGS

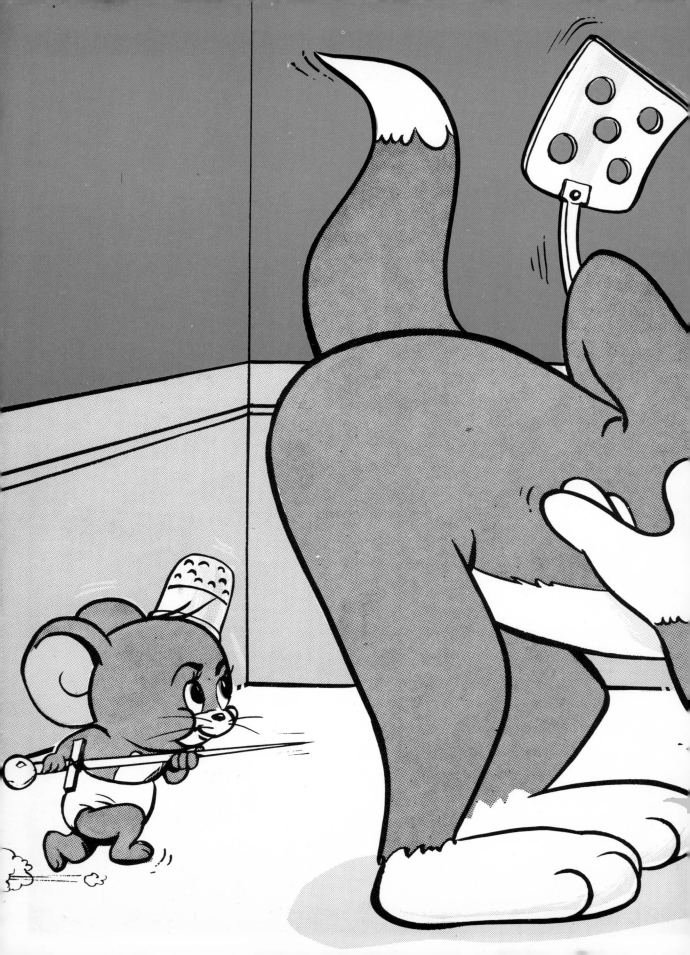